I Beheld His Glory!

I Beheld His Glory!

by " Cornelius the Centurion "
Newsman of Galilee

John Evans

1945

WILLETT, CLARK & COMPANY

CHICAGO   NEW YORK

Copyright, 1945, by

. JOHN EVANS

Reprinted by permission of The Chicago Tribune

To Ella James

Preface

CORNELIUS the Centurion appeared suddenly one day after a long search for someone who could write an eyewitness account of some of the most influential events ever recorded. I stumbled across him as I browsed through early chapters of Matthew. Acquaintance ripened into devotion to this lovable character.

Matthew did not introduce him to me by name but I quickly felt assured that I had found, after long quest, the man who might write a newsman's story of what happened long ago in Bethlehem, Jerusalem and Caesarea. An old world was dying, a new being born.

But who was Matthew's Centurion, this captain of Herod Antipas' police there in Capernaum? Obviously, despite his Roman citizenship, he was held in high esteem throughout Herod's Galilean realm. Matthew made it clear that this Centurion had a remarkable eye for essential details; he was diplomatic, or, rather, a politic man. Equally clear was his feeling for human matters.

But most policemen, especially police captains, are like that if they are good at their jobs. A bit hard and blunt, perhaps, but those characteristics are often assumed to shield a sympathetic understanding of the human situation. The best news reporters were trained during their police stints to see the human side, which is what most folks want to read about.

Literary efforts? No! Such are shunned. Reflective and editorial elements are out of range of men so trained. No poets or philosophers, they — nor politicians! The story, and the story only, is the thing. And the test of the story is whether or not it writes itself. Because this is so, the story has inherent power, unhampered by literary effort, personal opinion, or special pleading.

Well, just who was Matthew's Centurion, this almost forgotten Roman who may have been destined to open the doors of the primitive Christian church to the Gentiles? Luke had a Centurion, whom he named in Acts 10 as Cornelius. Luke was quite a bit better as a reporter than Matthew, who was more adept at covering speeches than in the more expert job of observing action. A nameless person might do for Matthew, but not for Luke, who had a much better idea of what plain people want to read about when newsworthy events take place.

I became assured, for my purposes at least, that Matthew's Centurion was Luke's Cornelius. Here, then, was my special correspondent. With Luke's help I also found some of Cornelius' friends — Joanna, wife of Chuza steward of Herod's household, and Mary of Magdala. Demetrius, Lentulus, and Linus entered the story on their own, just as Eleazar did. Finally Luke brought Peter into the often overlooked drama of Acts 10.

When I offered Cornelius' copy to the managing editor it pushed from page 1 accounts of the greatest war ever fought and crowded back in the paper current items of history's most complex and baffling era. Cornelius' correspondence was processed in identical manner with any other news items to reach rims of *Chicago Tribune* copy desks.

Many New Testament quotations are freely translated from the Greek, and the liturgical passages in the Epilogue are from the *Didaché*.

I acknowledge indebtedness to my friend, Rabbi G. George Fox, for valuable suggestions; to James H. Cobb for consultant research; to Benjamin Cohen for maps; and to my longtime associate, John L. Astley-Cock, for technical assistance.

JOHN EVANS

Chicago
Michaelmas 1944

I Beheld His Glory!

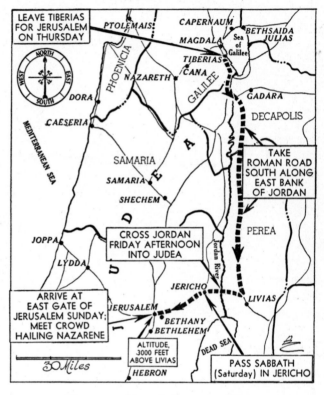

Labels within map:

LEAVE TIBERIAS FOR JERUSALEM ON THURSDAY

TAKE ROMAN ROAD SOUTH ALONG EAST BANK OF JORDAN

CROSS JORDAN FRIDAY AFTERNOON INTO JUDEA

ARRIVE AT EAST GATE OF JERUSALEM SUNDAY; MEET CROWD HAILING NAZARENE

ALTITUDE, 3000 FEET ABOVE LIVIAS

PASS SABBATH (Saturday) IN JERICHO

30 Miles

PTOLEMAIS · CAPERNAUM · BETHSAIDA JULIAS · MAGDALA · Sea of Galilee · TIBERIAS · CANA · GADARA · DECAPOLIS · PHOENICIA · NAZARETH · GALILEE · DORA · CAESERIA · MEDITERRANEAN SEA · SAMARIA · SAMARIA · SHECHEM · J U D E A · PEREA · JOPPA · CROSS JORDAN · Jordan River · LYDDA · JERICHO · LIVIAS · JERUSALEM · BETHANY · BETHLEHEM · DEAD SEA · HEBRON

ROUTE OF HEROD'S JERUSALEM TRIP

Broken arrows mark route of Herod from Tiberias to Jerusalem, and captions tell of developments on Holy Week trip in which his party met crowd strewing palms in path of lowly Nazarene on a donkey.

Prologue in Bethlehem

OUR caravan was rerouted at Gaza as it proceeded northward to accommodate my employer, Eleazar, a rich Judean glass merchant of Alexandria, intent on delivering luxury merchandise to customers in the new Zion district of Jerusalem in time for a winter festival.

But here we are, stalled in this miserable village of Bethlehem. Eleazar thinks the crowds which held us up will slacken so that we can proceed tomorrow. Seldom do caravans travel northward along this route. Usually they take the coastal plain, but despite nasty weather here in this mountainous country there is fascination in this historic land, even for a Roman.

Ostensibly, the crowds stalling us here are en route to a Roman census taking, but Eleazar, with a wink, spoke of today's anniversary of the country's liberation a century and a half ago from the tyranny of Syrian Greek despotism under Antiochus Epiphanes by Judas the Hammerer with a handful of Judean guerrillas. Even my tolerant country does not like its mandated peoples to recall their past victories any too vividly.

Since we left the coastal route our troubles mostly

I

were this incessant drizzle, chill winds, fog. The cold penetrates to the marrow, but last night's strange incident, together with Eleazar's stories about his peculiar people, has made up for some of the discomfort.

Eleazar, now on what he calls his last pilgrimage to the city of his fathers, warned against expecting any hospitality from his people here in Judea, above all in Jerusalem. They will be distant and aloof, he said, but he told me of their traditions in a way which made one feel kindly sympathy for those who remained here in this desolate and unproductive land in order to conserve a rich cultural and religious tradition reaching back more than a thousand years.

Here, off all main trade routes, and by holding firm against all outside influences, the garden of tradition blooms where nothing else will grow. Eleazar said the temple at Jerusalem really supports the whole of Judea. In addition to being a religious center it is virtually a bank with its own coinage, a wealthy institution that conquerors would like to plunder. Part of its riches is derived from profits in foreign exchange from pilgrims who are compelled to buy animals and other items for sacrifice only with temple coinage.

But Eleazar explained with a shrug that our caravan would be as comfortable in the open as in Bethlehem's leaky mud-roofed houses. He added that Jerusalem will hang out no welcome sign to me, a Roman on unofficial business. You see, he said, the sphere of influence of Rome is constantly widening just as Alexander's empire did three centuries ago. A bitter war and incredible feats of heroism by Judas and his guerrillas were necessary to win the freedom of this tiny commonwealth.

Now another conflict looms as the people on today's festival recall the Hammerer's exploits and look to the dynasty he established. Even though the Roman senate set up Herod's present throne in part to end that dynasty, the wily Herod married into the Hammerer's line. Herod is a sort of naturalized Jew, but is really a descendant of the hated Edomites, and how Judea loathes this " Edomite slave " who rules over it!

But he has kept the land peaceful and reasonably prosperous. Did he not keep Judea out of the hands of Cleopatra, and did he not quell the rebellion in Galilee with an iron hand? And did he not rebuild the temple and fortify Jerusalem against any assault?

Yes, but did he not rebuild Samaria into a hated Greek city, and help build foreign temples elsewhere? But his wickedness and pagan spirit are now catching up with him. He spends more and more time each year at Callirrhoe hot springs and is sick most of the time. His jealousies are becoming maniacal.

Recently he became suspicious of the ambitions of his sons, who, through their mother, are members of the Hammerer's dynasty and he is not. He summarily recalled them from Rome and executed two of his own sons as he put their mother to death twenty-two years ago. Herod strikes instantly and ruthlessly when he thinks his power is threatened.

3

But with all his violent temper and cruelty, the people are worried about what will happen when he dies. From accounts of his sickness, that time is not far off. Will the country then suffer partition and resulting civil violence leading to further intervention by Rome? A large section of the people, particularly in Galilee, want to attack now, just as the Hammerer did. But that means war, and the loss of temple revenue from pilgrims. Ruination would ensue.

Here in Bethlehem the main business is sheep raising. The sheep are certified by the priests for temple sacrifices and economic conditions are good. What they want more than anything else is peace, so they tolerate Herod but worry about the state of his health.

These worries were accentuated last night by a strange incident. Drivers heard a commotion in stables where our caravan animals are kept. We did not want to run into further trouble and delay so Eleazar and I went out, despite the late night chill, to see if something else might further stall us.

To our amazement the sky was clear, and a brilliant star not known to these people seemed to shine directly into one of the stables. On approaching we learned that a young woman from Galilee had become a mother in the stable, where the young woman and her husband had been forced to go because of the crowded village. Eleazar explained that a new and brilliant star would be one of the sure signs of the birth of David's divinely anointed descendant.

4

Then frightened shepherds began arriving in the village. They told of hearing heavenly song in the sky telling of peace to men of good will. While still terror-struck, they saw an angel who bade them be unafraid; that good news was breaking . . .

"For unto you is born this day in the city of David a Savior, which is the anointed of the Lord. And this shall be a sign unto you; ye shall find the babe wrapped in swaddling clothes, lying in a manger."

Awestricken, Eleazar whispered to me that Bethlehem is David's city; that here the great king would be born. He turned back to the stable, and I, following him, entered. The loveliness of the scene was unforgettable; the light of the star on two beautiful faces, mother and babe, with the glow forming a crown around the infant's head. The husband knelt before the manger in adoration.

Before parting from Eleazar for the short remainder of the night, I asked him if there should be anything to these strange portents. His moist eye glistened in the star's light.

"I think there is," he said. "I am sure of it."

Thirty-four years elapse between prologue and sequence. Cornelius, stranded by Eleazar's death, joined the imperial legions of Emperor Augustus. Rising from the ranks, he at last became a centurion. Herod the Great died in the year following the prologue. His kingdom was partitioned among three sons and a daughter, with Herod Archelaus over Judea, who was soon replaced by Roman procurators, and Herod Antipas over Galilee and Perea. As the sequence opens, Herod Antipas is on his way to Jerusalem.

Palm Sunday

OUR journey up to Jerusalem for the feast of the Passover in the company of Herod, Rome's puppet ruler of Galilee and Perea, was uneventful, except for a single incident late today just outside the city gate. As military aide to this ruler, it was my duty to clear a way through throngs en route to the feast, and I felt I had succeeded.

We departed four days ago from Tiberias, Herod's capital on the sea of Galilee, and proceeded southward through Perea, east of the Jordan river. Many hastening groups made way for us without unpleasantness, but some from the Decapolis and beyond, who were not Herod's subjects, grumbled wrathfully at him.

The sun is warm and the rainy season is about over. Farmers are making ready for the barley harvest in lowlands. With the Passover only six days away, they must hasten with their harvest because they must present the first tenth of the crop to the temple before the feast, else they will find trouble and delays in marketing the balance. Olive trees are in full leaf, and flower-covered hills are celebrating springtime almost breathlessly before the torrid summer sun bronzes them into barrenness.

Yesterday, the Sabbath, we rested in Jericho after crossing the Jordan Friday into Judea with its broken rockland. Passing the night in Jericho, we set out early this morning, the First day of the week, determined to complete the long climb up, up, to Jerusalem by midafternoon. Judea's history, which I have been trying to understand for many years, has been as tumultuous as its mountainous contour.

At present, Judea is ruled by Pontius Pilate, a Roman military governor whose title is procurator. He has made many mistakes during the four years of his rule, but despite his unpopularity with the people generally, he manages to keep the peace and to get along with those temple authorities who are his stooges.

But Herod and Pilate are at outs, largely because Herod hates anything Roman and Pilate hates anything Judean. Herod's attitude is not surprising because years ago Rome washed out of his princedom nearly all authority inherited from his father and reduced his power to that of tetrarch, which is his official designation in Rome. Fanned by his hatred for Pilate, Herod finds ironical pleasure in recounting Pilate's mistakes. One blunder especially amuses him.

To get Herod's point, which is hard for us Romans to understand, it must be realized that for the Judeans there is only one God, and his statues and pictures are never to be made. But with us, we have many gods, with every emperor beginning with Caesar Augustus also a god.

8

On nearly every corner in Rome, and in all the cities of our vast empire, images of various gods receive obeisance of their devotees. But among Judeans, this is the worst of sins. Unaware of this — and it should be remembered that Rome pledged religious liberty to Judea — the very first official act of Pilate was to post the image of Emperor Tiberius, together with the sacred eagles of the Roman legions, in a tower a stone's throw from the temple in Jerusalem.

With ironical laughter, Herod recalled this blunder just as we set foot in Judea from the Jordan river which bounds the country on the east.

" The crazy Roman," Herod roared. " Erect an image of the emperor in the tower of Antonia, will he? Yes, but was his face red when he had to jerk it out again. Roman emperor and eagles backing out! Pfui! And the fool used temple shekels to build the new Jerusalem aqueduct. He made some kind of a private deal with High Priest Caiaphas, to do it!

" That's a team for you! Pilate and Caiaphas! When Caiaphas' nose itches, Pilate sneezes. Both are in bad with most people, and they'd better pull together, but I'll bet my money on Caiaphas in the long run."

The elevation of Caiaphas to the high priesthood by a predecessor of Pilate's a decade ago was a scandalous affair. Annas, father-in-law of Caiaphas, still boss of the temple hierarchy, was then the high priest, but because he would not give in to Roman demands the military governor threw him out and named Caiaphas in his

9

place. Caiaphas' appointment was unpopular from the start and it is probable that most Judeans still regard Annas as the high priest.

Thus, if the political scene is a mess in Judea, the religious situation is not much better. And now comes the crisis — a crowded Passover season!

Vengefully foreseeing Pilate's troubles during the week, Herod had sought more and more speed through the lower faultlands. As higher country was reached, and Bethany passed, I had increasing trouble in clearing a way through the crowds. Finally, just below the ascent to the east portal of Jerusalem, known as the Gate of the Lily, we appeared to be stalled.

A vast throng had surged down from the city singing a joyous welcome to another group which was proceeding toward the city. When the two met and refused to give way to Herod I dismounted and forced my way into the crowd to find the cause of the demonstration. This I soon learned, for all hallelujahs were for one who was mounted on a donkey. Palms were waved over his head and flowers and bright garments are strewn in his way.

Hailing him as the new king, the son of David, the entire throng then struck up a chant beginning with the ancient word " Hosannah! " " Save us now! "

" Save us now!
Blessed is he who comes in the name of the Lord;
Blessed is the approaching kingdom of our father
David.
Save us in the heights of heaven! "

Pressing closer, it startled me to see who was receiving the regal welcome as one anointed of the Lord! It was that strange young man of Nazareth of whom I had heard much in Galilee. I saw him first in Capernaum where I was garrisoned until about a year ago. Although I never had actually met the young man, I had heard him speak in the new synagogue where I was always welcome, Roman that I am.

I am unable to describe the power of his personality other than to say that to be near him made me realize the unworthiness of my life. The people of Capernaum, and many in near-by Magdala, held him in deep reverence. Despite his great kindliness I could not persuade myself to greet him.

On pressing closer to the center of the crowd I was amazed to discover that Joanna, wife of Chuza, steward of Herod's household, was in the young man's attendant group. Also, that street woman of Magdala, Mary, as well as a number of fisherfolk I had seen with him in Galilee. I recall that when Demetrius, my orderly, was stricken, and the doctors could do no more for him, Joanna had asked the young man, who had great power over sickness, to heal him.

When I learned that the young man was on his way to my house I felt that I could not induce myself to admit him, due to the curious spell he holds over me. I sent word to the young man, begging him to do what he could at a distance. Demetrius improved at once and still serves me.

Here in the shadow of Jerusalem's gate the young

man appeared to have aged. He accepted the crowd's enthusiasm, but the verve of other days was replaced by what seemed to be either fatigue or serious trouble. He started to make his way toward me, but I could not withstand his glance. With a catch in my throat I turned aside, routed the tetrarch's retinue around the young man's throng, and reported to Herod.

He was first to speak:

"A fine day we live in," he exclaimed sarcastically, "when a son of Herod the Great must turn aside for rabble. But Pilate will have plenty on his hands this week, mark my word."

Monday

THIS last year as military aide to Herod compensates for my advancing years, especially after three decades of garrison duty throughout the Roman world. Besides, I am getting a kick out of my first visit to Jerusalem during this great Passover season.

The city is overrun by pilgrims from everywhere and money gushes over tradesmen's counters. Were it not for its pilgrim trade, Jerusalem would soon have grass growing in its crooked, narrow streets.

Demetrius and I are quartered in the Hasmonean palace, where Herod resides when he is in Jerusalem, just a stone's throw westward from the temple across a ravine. This old palace appears to be a monument to the dying hopes for a dynasty which would restore a Judean empire as vast as that of the ancient king, David. Herod, only a stepson of the Hasmonean line, holds tenaciously to his thin Hasmonean connections and traditions.

The story of that dynasty is complex, but only less so than Herod's relationship with it. Through Herod's stepmother, the Hasmonean line runs back two hundred years through the greatest modern Judean family. It

13

was founded on the magical name of Judas the Hammerer, who defeated Antiochus Epiphanes. That hated Greek had wrecked Judean religious traditions and had defiled the temple. No name in recent centuries is so revered as the Hammerer's.

However, the secondary line, of which Herod is a descendant, stems from his cunning Edomite grandfather, Herod Antipater, a petty desert chieftain who had guessed right as to who would win the world war between Julius Caesar and Pompey. Herod Antipater bet on Julius Caesar, for whom his tribe fought, and then reaped a kingly reward when Caesar won. But how the Judeans loathe the Herodian line with its loose morals and patronizing gestures toward Judean traditions and institutions!

Herod's trip up to the Passover was regarded by him merely as just one of those appointments he ought to keep for the looks of things; a gesture!

" You see," he told us with a wink, " I want to see how the Roman fool, Pontius Pilate, gets by with the Passover crowds this year. Just let some crazy Galilean reformer start something again and Pilate and High Priest Caiaphas will have their hands full of riots. Jerusalem's bosses may get by this year — but wait till next year, or thereafter! "

As Herod said this, thoughts of the throng that welcomed the young man of Nazareth, a Galilean, filled my mind. There was a puzzling difference between that group and the other crowds we passed on the way. The people who pressed about the young Galilean would not step aside, even for a Hasmonean heir. I cannot get over the impulse I had at one moment to join them, especially when I espied Joanna among the young man's throng. She is a wise old woman, and one who has always been kind to me.

In fact, all Judeans of Galilee have been good to me. Often they have told me of their fierce love for the temple and for their ancient traditions. With them, I find myself distressed over stories of decadence and mismanagement of the temple under Rome's High Priest Caiaphas and his gang.

It was with mixed feeling this afternoon that, with Demetrius, I crossed the stone bridge over the ravine toward the temple for the sacrifices. Missing was the kindly synagogue greeting as I entered the temple's outer court. Before me was a raucous scene.

Throngs seethed through the court, bargaining and haggling for the purchase of sacrificial animals. Scores of priests were making ready for the ritual slaughter of the creatures which previously had been certified for sacrifices by the hierarchy. Lambs, bullocks, and turtle-doves were confined to pens around the booths of concession operators. Brisk also was the sale of sacrificial oil, meal, wine, and incense. Prices for these sacrificial items soared as high as the traffic would bear; far above other markets in the city.

Moreover, exchange rates for temple coinage, necessary for sacrificial purchases, are outrageous and no attention is paid to the protests against those who control the temple monopoly. That monopoly is protected

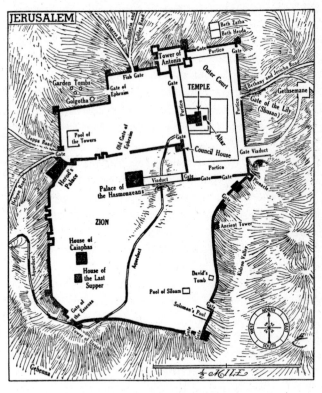

WHERE NAZARENE CREATED SENSATION

Map of Jerusalem, locating temple where a young Nazarene caused a sensation by crying that His Father's house had been made a " den of thieves."

by Roman arms, under agreements between Rome and the Judean national council, the political Sanhedrin. Scorned were the protests of outraged pilgrims as they longed for other days before Roman scalawags got control of temple affairs.

All this traffic and commotion within the temple precincts was the cause of the universal dismay among the people over the present temple administration and its Rome-appointed high priest.

A sudden outcry pierced the din. It was as though a hurricane had struck. Booths toppled, lambs scurried here and there, doves took to wing, and temple shekels clattered on the pavement. Concession operators clutched for their possessions amid milling pilgrims. At first, struck rigid by the swift outbreak, Demetrius and I drew our swords, seeking cause of the uproar.

A figure dashed across the pavement, swinging a lash on the backs of concessionaires, smashing booths, and overturning money-changing tables. As I rushed toward this person, a strange, tense calm fell with the same suddenness with which the bedlam had begun.

Standing there, confronting the throng which had frozen in its tracks, face ashen in anger, lash in one hand, the other raised high as though he would still a storm, was that young man of Nazareth!

His voice rang out in the stillness:

" Is it not written, ' My house shall be a house of prayer for all the nations '? But you have made it a den of thieves."

Tuesday

WHILE I am certain that the young man of Nazareth faces trouble, even possible execution, yet nothing has happened of note since his sensational exploit yesterday in the temple.

Despite absence of orders from Pontius Pilate, who is responsible for keeping the peace, I detailed Demetrius to the temple under instructions to keep his eyes open and report back. Should yesterday's scenes have occurred at any other place in the empire, the military would be under immediate orders for summary arrests. But not so here!

This is different; so much so as to present humorous aspects to a Roman observer. In spite of my anxiety for the young man's welfare, I have caught myself chuckling over temple concession operators' expert form as they dived for rolling shekels or skidded across the pavement in their dash for the fleeing lambs' hind legs.

Two things, however, mystify me as I reconstruct that scene: Why was it that I, a Roman officer of the law, was in some way constrained from arresting the young man; secondly, how did he manage to disappear so quickly after he had spoken?

18

As I puzzled over these questions, I noticed Joanna approaching from the temple. The sparkling little old lady listened to my questions, her eyes twinkling.

"There was nothing strange in the young man's disappearance," Joanna said, half mockingly. "You Romans often go off the deep end when you are in Judea. The young man merely walked out of the temple and proceeded to the home of friends in Bethany. Indeed, if you wish to arrest him, you will find him in the temple at this very moment."

I protested that the last thing I should ever want to do would be to arrest the Nazarene. But why, I asked her, should he endanger himself by re-entering the temple today, knowing the wrath of temple authorities against him? Joanna replied that, being a Roman, I probably wouldn't understand with "my boyish mind and naïve directness."

"You Romans are just little boys grown up into big bodies," Joanna said. "But if you will listen carefully I will try to explain it. You of the west are young. You know how to fight, administer civil law, and govern a whole world very well; we of the east are old folk, reflective, who see everything in the light of our mature religious culture.

"You of Rome have dreamed and fought for your imperial city that it might become the empire it now is. To what end? Materialistic magnificence! But what is that?

"You appear to rule over Judea, and over Judeans

19

scattered throughout your empire, and in lesser civil matters you succeed very well. Only to minds of the immature are civil laws of first importance. But among our people of Judea who are old from their cradles, your superficial rule is unimportant. Judea and Jerusalem are symbols of another kind of empire which military might can never dominate.

" Within each of us is a holy commonwealth — foretaste of the kingdom of heaven. It is in our marrow. You cannot understand it, but it is there. Drive us from this rockpile into Babylon, raze our temple, and the fortress of our sacred commonwealth becomes impregnable. Whensoever we may make government our only aim, we shall fail, but even then our ideal commonwealth will persist. While you of the west become senile, we rejuvenate.

" Pilate, with the aid of all of Caesar's legions, scarcely could have arrested the young Nazarene yesterday. His action in the temple was popular. But there is more to it than that. Pilate dared not trespass, for then both people, and the temple authorities whom the young man outraged, would have turned on Pilate. Far sooner would all Judeans, from Caiaphas to the lowliest, see the temple destroyed rather than a Caesar and materialistic might violate its sanctity."

Joanna's explanation helped somewhat. But I was assured that the high priest and his schemers would resent the action of the young man and I was puzzled as to what means the high priest and his hirelings, and the political Sanhedrin, would use to proceed against the Nazarene. She nodded assent when I suggested stealth, and urged that I should go to the temple at once to see if various groups were not now trying to trap him into criminal admissions.

The greatest crimes against Rome are sedition and treason, whereas the highest capital crime among Judeans is blasphemy, but blasphemy has no standing in Roman law, under which all capital crimes are tried in Judea. As I crossed the bridge toward the temple I recalled the regal greeting of the throng when the young man approached the city on the First day of the week. That, I thought, could lead to a seditious admission of kingship, and constitute the first step toward a popular movement to restore in Judea the ancient kingdom of the great David.

The outer court had changed. The booths and exchange tables were there, but the concession operators were deprived of customers. Looking farther, I saw the reason; the usual throng of pilgrims was gathered around the young Nazarene near the east portico, listening intently. Pressing into the throng, I heard a questioner ask:

" Is it lawful to pay tribute to Caesar, or not? "

The question put the young man on the spot. If he answered yes, he would alienate the vast majority of his followers who hate Rome. Should he answer in the negative, he would be accused of sedition against Rome.

The crowd became very quiet. What would he say?

" Show me a penny," the young man replied quietly. Holding it high for all to see, he asked:

" Whose is this image and superscription? "

" Caesar's," was the instant reply from his questioner.

" Render therefore to Caesar the things that are Caesar's," the young man said, " and to God the things that are God's."

The crowd seemed to melt away. Moving with a group toward the temple gate, I heard one remark sadly to his companions:

" He won every tilt with his accusers today, but I fear they will never rest until they convict him and have him sentenced to death."

Maundy Thursday

TWO disturbing incidents today cost me the sense of well-being which I enjoyed earlier in the week as I looked forward toward tomorrow night's opening of the great Judean festival of liberation, the Passover.

But today there came a summons from my former commanding officer, Military Tribune Rufus, of the Second battalion from Italy, to appear for active duty at the garrison in the tower of Antonia. Besides that, came new information from Joanna which made me fearful for the fate of the young Nazarene.

All was relatively quiet yesterday and I had begun to believe that the young man's exploit in lashing the temple concessionaires and their bosses as thieves would be overlooked by High Priest Caiaphas and that he might escape punishment.

Now, I am doubtful, for Joanna's story, which was told to her by John, one of the Nazarene's twelve most trusted followers, is a disturbing one. John, despite his fidelity to the young man, appears to have some kind of an in with Annas. John had learned of the existence of a cabal against the Nazarene in the inner circle of the political Sanhedrin.

Joanna made it clear that the action of the Nazarene in overturning booths and exchange counters in the temple was not the only count held against him by the chief priests. They have been determined for a long time to destroy him because of his huge followings, which they regard as a threat to the peace of Jerusalem and damaging to the good standing of the temple crowd in the sight of Rome.

Caiaphas was reported to have argued that if the death of one Galilean would assure peace in Jerusalem and guarantee the city's continued protection under the tolerant eagles of Emperor Tiberius, then that Galilean ought to die. Some time ago the high priests and rulers of the temple tried to entrap the Nazarene in seditious speech.

Once they caught him in what they called a blasphemous utterance, making himself the anointed of the Lord, the Messiah. He miraculously escaped being lynched, and it was fortunate for the temple leaders that the young man was not stoned. Otherwise, they would have had a popular martyr on their hands with serious disturbances sure to follow.

From what Joanna learned from John it seemed that the Sanhedrin clique had planned to await an occasion after the Passover to bring the Nazarene to trial. By that time the pilgrims would be gone and the city quiet. But something else has intervened, demanding immediate action. She said it appeared to be John's belief that new information against the Nazarene had come from a hidden source.

Furthermore, Joanna learned of desertion of one group of the Nazarene's followers yesterday. These are Galilean firebrands who are always watched closely during greater festivals because of their revolutionary tendencies. They hate Rome fiercely and can see no reason why Roman rule should not be overthrown at once. The reason for their desertion of the Nazarene, who they had believed might be their anointed deliverer, was his approval of paying tribute taxes to Caesar.

While his answer to his temple questioners was correct as to his views on separation of church and Roman state, yet this admission that taxes might lawfully be paid to Caesar lost him his most violently inclined supporters, probably one of the Twelve among them, who had reported secretly to Annas. They wagged their heads, saying, "This man who would pay tribute to an idolatrous emperor is not our kind of anointed leader." When these zealots, who were the most likely to start a riot, were thus shown to have discarded the Nazarene, the temple clique felt much safer in going ahead with its plot.

On reporting to Rufus, I was assigned to lead a special detachment to guard the house of High Priest Caiaphas, clearing all neighboring streets at nightfall. Safe-conduct into the high priest's house was issued to only one person, a certain Judas, of Kirioth, a village in Judea south of Jerusalem. This man is not of Galilee, and my hope was raised that possibly my assignment did not bear on the Nazarene's case, as I had heard only of Galileans in the young man's most intimate following.

I was told that the appearance of the man of Kirioth, or the Iscariot, was to be the signal for me to send a runner to call up heavier detachments, of both the Second battalion and the temple guard, under Rufus' direct command. Night fell; hours passed. Then a single figure slunk up the street northward toward the house of Caiaphas. He was stopped and passed successively by the sentries of my detachment.

On his arrival at the door of the house where I was stationed he whispered hoarsely, " I am the Iscariot." As a light through the open door shone on his face, he avoided my gaze. Hastening through the portal, he trembled; his swarthy face was drawn and pallid!

I had seen that face before. The Iscariot was a member of the young man's company when, with palms and flowers, hallelujahs and hosannahs, the Nazarene had been accorded his acclaim on the First day of the week.

Here, thought I, is the source of the hidden information. A betrayal!

Good Friday

EVENTS sometimes play cruel pranks. For example, what I had anticipated as a pleasant tourist's holiday in this unique city, with its long history and strange daily life, has turned to tragedy.

As my detachment now stands guard in this tower above the temple where priests are making ready for the sacrifices of Passover lambs, that young Nazarene, convicted of treason against the person of Tiberius as emperor, is being executed on a cross outside the city wall.

From this tower I could glance over the Gate of Ephraim to that barren hill and see three crosses, one of which bears his body. A centurion dare not weep and I averted my gaze from the scene.

Last night after the Twelve had supped their last together, the infamous Iscariot had left the group to fulfill his agreement with Caiaphas.

For money he had agreed to lead strong detachments under the command of Rufus to an unfrequented garden near the Jericho road, where the Nazarene would go for

27

meditation and where an arrest on the charges which the temple bosses had trumped up could be made. Few of the Nazarene's admiring throng would be about at that late hour to make a disturbance.

Hearings before former High Priest Annas and High Priest Caiaphas and an inner clique of the political Sanhedrin during the remaining night hours were planned, to be followed by an early morning arraignment before Pilate, long before pilgrim throngs stirred in the streets.

The temple gang expected a speedy conviction and a sentence of death, with plenty of time to carry out the execution before today's sunset marked the unusual coincidence of the Passover feast with the Sabbath.

But a hitch caused their plans to miscarry. Although the chief priests at last won their case, and the Nazarene was turned over to the military for execution, Pilate had shown great hesitancy in agreeing to demands for the young man's life. I, as a Roman, knew better than the Judeans the cause of this strange reluctance to act against the young man.

Centurion Lentulus, successor to my command in the Second battalion, was assigned charge of the execution. Lentulus, a hard-bitten veteran like myself, has had ample experience in such matters.

Once our battalion crucified five hundred rebels in Pontus. The place looked like a forest of weird trees by the time the last wretch had been spiked to his cross.

But that was during the last days of the reign of

Caesar Augustus! Since the accession of Tiberius to the imperial throne of Rome such mass executions have ceased. Under the new colonial policy a governor's administrative capacity is brought into question when insurrection breaks out.

Tiberius issued stern orders to his colonial governors to protect their peoples against boodling Roman officials who, under Augustus, were often the cause of serious disorders.

The governors were to see to it that the individual native also has protection against improper arrest and trial for lesser offenses by native authorities, with a capital offender to appear only before the governor or such tribunal as he might elect.

Tiberius' policy did not arise from a tender heart. Far from it! What he wants is taxes, and taxes are not the fruition of revolt and insurrection. Quite the opposite!

Any miscarriage of justice to reach Tiberius' ears is quickly investigated, and the governor, if found blameworthy, is removed and disgraced throughout the empire. But the emperor's policy is hard on dispensers of political patronage, and it underlies much of the political strife so far in Tiberius' stormy and unhappy reign.

Nevertheless, Pilate's boss in Rome is a hard man and Pilate was on the spot this morning when the Nazarene was set before him here in Pilate's judgment hall. Before him was a ticklish case which bode well for riot or insurrection. Should such occur, the governor's administrative ability would be impeached before the stern emperor, with disgrace and forfeiture of knighthood.

But if a tough-minded emperor faced him on the one hand, on the other were the relentless temple bosses, intent on doing away with the Nazarene who had exposed temple abuses, and whose mighty works and simple, godly teaching attracted throngs of followers everywhere.

The trial dragged, with Pilate hedging and delaying, and the accusing priests becoming frantic. One accusation after another was dismisssed after the Nazarene had been questioned by Pilate within the judgment hall. The crowds of midforenoon now filled the streets.

Would they be rallied by some supporter of the Nazarene to drown out the shouts of " Crucify him! Crucify him! " from throats of temple concessionaires?

The same thought must at last have occurred to Pilate. Riots before his judgment seat? Impossible! Again he brought the Nazarene from the hall to confront his accusers; a last chance! Again the frantic cries, " Crucify him! " A figure crept close to Pilate and shouted:

" If you release this fellow you are no friend of Caesar's. Anyone who claims to be a king, speaks against the emperor."

This charge was the climax. It was treason against the person of the emperor. Pilate yielded. The young man quickly was dragged away.

Musing, I reviewed the tumultuous scenes with the

false, trumped-up charges of the morning, as I paced the observation ramp. I had scarcely noted a strange darkness which had fallen on the city, though it could be no later than the ninth hour, midafternoon.

As I was about to call for the lighting of torches, the tower of Antonia shook beneath us. Built within recent years to withstand the earthquakes common to this region, it was, I knew, safe, but I feared for the old palace of the Hasmoneans, where Herod was residing. I would go there at once, I thought, and dispatch my men to the temple to prevent a possible stampede.

As I moved past a west window, my eyes were drawn toward the hill beyond Ephraim's gate where light was breaking on the darkness. Three crosses still there, but deserted! Light advanced as I quickened my pace toward the old palace. Streets were filled with hurrying folk. The terror with which the darkness and earthquake had stricken them was diminishing with the advancing light.

A detachment of soldiers strode wearily past me toward the tower, their commanding officer following. It was Centurion Lentulus! He appeared broken and tried not to heed my salute. Failing, he came toward me and clasped my hands in his. His lips moved as if to speak.

Standing there, both speechless, we heard a woman speak. It was Joanna, dry of eye, still sprightly beyond her years.

" You spoke rightly out there, Centurion Lentulus,"

she said, pointing to the hill beyond Ephraim's gate. " He is the Son of God!   Lift weight from your hearts. All is not over!   Increase your faith! "

Lentulus then regained his speech.   Said he:

" I believe!   He is the Son of God! "

Easter

HE is risen! Joanna's prediction that "all is not over" has come true. I saw the young man of Nazareth with my own eyes. I heard him speak. His blessing was of Peace. He told us to tell the good news to the whole world.

How shall I relate the facts of today, which began dismally enough, other than to write down faithfully what I saw?

I had arisen long before the dawn this morning and had gone out on the high gallery in the tower of Antonia overlooking the temple. Sleep for me has been elusive since the Nazarene was executed out yonder on the hill beyond Ephraim's gate. Besides, another of Jerusalem's earthquakes had made sleep difficult.

Looking down from the high gallery I could discern priests moving about the court of the temple through the gray of the dawn, making ready for the morning sacrifice of the First day of the week.

On each of the four corners of the roof of the temple were three trumpeters ready to herald the sacrifice to the four winds of the earth. They awaited a signal from a priest who, high in the pinnacle opposite the tower, gazed across Jordan above the dark hills of Moab for the first gleam of the sun, the moment for the sacrifice to begin.

The ritual of the morning sacrifice for the whole people called for the lamb to be slain and offered on the altar. Together with the incense offering, and the consuming of the meal and drink offerings, the liturgy of the First day of the week requires the singing of the ancient psalm of enthronement, the enthronement of the Lord as King of the universe:

" The earth is the Lord's, and the fullness thereof . . .
  Lift up your heads, O ye gates,
  And be ye lifted up, ye everlasting doors;
  That the King of Glory may come in. . . ."

As I contemplated the activity below, Centurion Lentulus approached. He, too, had spent sleepless hours and spoke of the earthquake. He inquired about my presence in Jerusalem, and as I began to recount events of the months of my retirement from the Second battalion, the trumpets sounded their fanfare below us.

A gleam of the sun had shot across the hills of the plain of Moab. Priest-borne torches glowed red against the courts below. Soon the sound of singing arose from the temple. It was interspersed with the sound of silvery trumpets, calling the assemblage to prayer.

Aloft came the closing words of the psalm:

" Who is this King of Glory? Even the Lord . . ."

But the final words were drowned out by armed men running toward us in the tower gallery. Breathlessly they reported to Lentulus, their officer:

"The earthquake, sir," their spokesman said. "It tore away the stone which had been sealed into the door of the sepulcher. We were felled as with a blow. On regaining ourselves we saw the stone had been rolled aside. On it sat One we scarce could gaze upon for the brightness of his raiment and countenance. Though he seemed to smile at us we fled.

"We were confused, sir, but as we began our flight we passed two men, running toward the tomb. We heard one say, 'He is risen.'"

Lentulus dismissed the detachment and we hastened toward the sepulcher, set in its lovely rock garden. Bright flowers smiled from every crevice. Birds piped their most brilliant songs through the fresh spring air to the fast rising sun.

There before us was an empty tomb, the round stone door rolled aside. The seal of the Roman empire upon it was smashed!

We turned back toward the city, speechless, and sought Joanna. Radiant, she told her story:

"Very early before the dawn, Mary of Magdala, Mary, mother of James, and other women went to the sepulcher with spices which we had prepared. We found the stone rolled away from the tomb, and entering in we found not the body of the Lord. While we were

35

perplexed, two men stood by us in dazzling apparel. We were frightened and bowed down our faces.

" Said they unto us: ' Why seek ye the living among the dead? He is not here. He is risen: remember how he told you when yet he was in Galilee, saying that the Son of man must be delivered up into the hands of sinful men, and be crucified, and rise again? '

" We remembered the words, and returned from the tomb and told these things to the Eleven and to the rest. Some doubted, but Peter and John at once ran to the sepulcher after we had told them, and they, too, found it empty."

Joanna added that all the young man's friends would meet after sundown and invited us to join them.

After darkness had settled on the city, Joanna bade us go with her to a house where his followers were to meet behind closed doors for fear of the temple authorities. We gladly went.

Many of the first doubts about the risen Lord had been dispelled. The Nazarene already had appeared to Clopas and another follower on the road to Emmaus. They told their story to our group.

Then even as their narrative was given, it happened! The risen Nazarene appeared in the midst of our company; his pierced hands raised in blessing as he spoke:

" Peace be unto you: As the Father hath sent me, even so send I you. Receive ye the Holy Spirit: whosesoever sins ye forgive, they are forgiven unto them; whosesoever sins ye retain, they are retained. Go ye into all the world and preach the good news to the whole creation."

I turned toward Lentulus, who had fallen to his knees. He murmured softly:

" Lord Jesus, I'll go."

Six years elapse between sequence and epilogue. Cornelius now resides in Caesarea, in complete retirement.

Epilogue in Caesarea

TODAY brought the feast of Saturn to a close. In previous years, since my return to this Roman city, my household and I entered into the gaiety of the season. This year the crippling pains in my bones, which five years ago sent me back from Tiberias into complete retirement, crimped any frolicking horseplay for me.

Thus for us the observance simmered down to a few candles lighted in honor of our ancient god of Latium. Perhaps it was fortunate that I was forced to spare myself because today, for the first time during my long years in Syria, I was host at meat to Judeans. While I always have been on friendliest terms with them, yet never before had I been given opportunity to break bread with them. Ancient tradition prevents such consort between Judeans and persons of other ancestry.

Beyond the entertainment of most unusual dinner guests, two other things took place. One was a leave-taking of commingled heartbreak and joy. The other event was similar to the reappearance of the young Nazarene when he quietly entered that upper room to greet his followers after his execution and acclaimed resurrection. That he was truly in my house today I now have no doubt although my eye did not perceive him.

The leave-taking was that of my old friend, Centurion Lentulus, and his orderly, Linus, as they set out for Antioch and Rome on orders from Vitellius, imperial legate of Syria with residence in Antioch. A fortnight ago Vitellius ordered Pilate's summary dismissal as military governor of Samaria and Judea. His meddling in temple affairs, this time in Samaria, had brought about his downfall.

On learning of his dismissal Pilate ordered Lentulus and his detachment to Caesarea from Jerusalem, where he had long been in command of the garrison in the tower of Antonia. My joy was great when Lentulus entered my house and for a time it seemed certain he would be stationed here permanently.

But just before today's unusual meal the order came from the legate sending him to Rome forthwith. It is doubtful, in view of the present chaos in Rome, if he will ever be returned to Syria. Things became so bad in our imperial city that Emperor Tiberius pulled out of Rome in disgust and now resides in self-imposed exile at Capri while affairs of state are in the hands of Sejanus, his chief minister of state.

Even the few days I had with Lentulus meant much to me. Moreover, he was formally commissioned in my house today to carry the teachings of the Nazarene's new way to Rome. But until his arrival I could scarcely say that I had a real religion, despite my interest in the synagogue and my observance of various Roman feasts, such as today's Saturnalia or the springtime's Bacchanalia, when buds swell and these Syrian hills take on their brief cloak of green.

One of those Bacchanalian days is unforgettable — that springtide sunrise after that long night in the tower when one of Jerusalem's earthquakes struck and, with Lentulus, I hurried to the garden beyond Ephraim's gate to find that tomb empty, its stone door rolled aside.

But I had not connected that event with religion — a religion like that of the temple — or even with the Bacchanalia. My tender regard for the young man who had risen from that tomb had not been religious; he only awed me. Quite different was my interest in the Galilean from my devotion to Bacchus! Bacchus has his points as the god of wine even though the crude and thoughtless often debauch his feast.

Bacchus pointed to a promise of life, an immortal life, and appeared to make good his assurance when at his feast the cup is raised to lip. The ensuing glow of the body was the symbol of his life one might share — and we of Rome demand life tingling to finger tip, assuring union with a god and partnership in his immortality. The religion of Bacchus was a yearning for life.

Today I found it!

Lentulus and Linus now carry that new life to the imperial city, where it will spread over the whole earth. But I shall never see them again.

In order to relate today's amazing event I must go

back and explain that my last days here in Caesarea have been lonely. There is not even a synagogue here. All are Romans, Greeks, and Syrians. The nearest synagogue on the coast is in the Judean city of Joppa, a day's journey, and I am a crippled old man!

True, my household has much knowledge of the Nazarene and we all, including Demetrius, revere him as a person of great nobility to whom we owed some kind of obligation. But we could not be sure what that obligation might be.

Then, at last, Lentulus and Linus came. They, together with the entire garrison, had entered the Nazarene's new way. But, sadly, those devoted soldiers also had been isolated by the nature of their duties as well as by their nationality.

They were Romans, while nearly all others who follow in the new way are Judeans from almost everywhere except Jerusalem's temple groups. Large numbers are from Galilee, where Rome is hated as bitterly as either Herod or the temple gang in Jerusalem.

Moreover, a great number of these Judeans speak only the Greek language. They were educated in Greek schools from Alexandria to Macedonia. They now are tradesmen, exporters, craftsmen, lawyers — pilgrims to Jerusalem, full of zeal for the law and traditions of their fathers despite their turn to the new way under the preaching of Peter and others of the Nazarene's most intimate followers.

In a way they became men of two religions, clinging

to the ancient ways while reaching for the new life assured by the risen Nazarene. They were taught from temple porches where Romans did not feel free to go. Fellowship of a common table was impossible, even though a meal of sacred meaning was the central observance. But of that meal Lentulus and his men could learn nothing.

Besides, the new adherent must submit to the initiatory rite called baptism, commanded by the Nazarene when last he met his followers. Romans were not admitted to this rite.

" Can only Judeans follow in the new way? " sadly asked Lentulus. " They themselves are glad for our reverence of the risen Nazarene but they, too, are baffled when fellowship in his name arises in our minds. They know we adore him, too, but they are helpless. They truly long to let us come with them but cannot. They know the whole empire will sometime follow his way could this nationalistic barrier be lifted."

Lentulus told me of the spread of the word to Joppa, where the great synagogue is the center of the new teaching. Peter is there now, he said, instructing throngs.

I pondered these things, and first thought of appealing to Peter. Foolish idea! Obviously, I am too feeble to make the journey and then, even though Peter should remember me from old Capernaum days, what could either of us do about the matter? If ever the Romans are to be admitted it can only be when Judeans bid them.

Only the Nazarene himself can bring about such a

miracle. He still lives, somewhere, and Lentulus assured me that the young Galilean is God. Why not pray to him?

My knees scarcely reached the floor when a strange sensation came over me. Seemingly I heard a voice. I listened!

"Cornelius," I heard the voice say. I looked up and saw a radiant messenger.

"What is it, sir?" I asked.

"Your prayers and charities," said he, "are remembered before God. Now send men to Joppa for a man named Simon, who is called Peter. He is entertained by a tanner, also named Simon, whose house is close by the sea."

The messenger departed. I called Demetrius and Linus, telling them all that had happened, and dispatched them to Joppa. Today, the third after their departure, they returned. Simon Peter and a number of Judeans were with them. They entered my house without hesitation, but I, overcome with joy, knelt at Peter's feet. He reached down and took me by the hand.

"Get up!" he said. "I, too, am only human."

I then explained all — told him how I had been instructed to send for him, and bade him speak to us all as he might be led.

"Now I really understand," said Peter, "that God shows no discrimination, welcomes the man of any race or nation who reveres him and does what is right. He has

44

sent his message to Israel's descendants and made the good news of peace known to them through the risen Christ. He is Lord of us all."

As Peter retold the story of the Nazarene a strange glowing warmth seemed to fill me until I no longer could restrain my speech. I declared my belief in the Lord as my God and while I spoke others were also proclaiming their faith, so much so that the Judeans in Peter's company seemed amazed that this special gift of God had been given likewise to Romans.

Then asked Peter: " Shall anyone forbid water to baptize this people on whom the Holy Spirit has descended? "

Following our baptism, while Peter was further instructing us in the new way, a runner from Vitellius entered. He bore the legate's command that Lentulus should seize Pilate at once and forthwith lead him to Antioch for orders before proceeding to Rome.

Evening approached and I summoned servants to prepare quickly a meal for the whole house.

When all had eaten Peter arose, proclaiming a Thanksgiving assembly of believers, and promised instruction in the Giving of Thanks. During the devotions he would commission Lentulus and Linus as bearers of the good news to Rome and the whole world.

He took the cup of wine in his hand and, before offering it to the assembly, said:

" We continually give thanks to Thee, our Father, for

45

the sacred vine of David Thy servant which Thou hast caused us to know through Christ Thy Son. To Thee be the glory for evermore."

He took bread in his hands and reverently broke it into fragments, saying:

" We continually give thanks to Thee, our Father, for the life and knowledge which Thou hast made known to us through Christ Thy Son. To Thee be glory for evermore. Just as this broken bread was scattered upon the mountains and has been gathered into one, so may Thy assembly be drawn from the corners of the earth into Thine own kingdom. For Thine is the glory and the power through Jesus Christ, forever."

Peter then caused Lentulus and Linus to kneel before the whole assembly and placed his hands on their heads, calling for prayers of all on them as bearers of the eternal life of Jesus to the whole world. He then offered thanks for the sacred meal:

" We continually give thanks to Thee, Holy Father, for Thy Holy Name, which Thou madest to dwell in our hearts, and for the knowledge and faith and death-lessness which Thou causest us to know through Christ Thy Son. To Thee be glory forever.

" Thou Ruler over all hast made everything for the sake of Thy name, both food and drink Thou hast given to men for enjoyment that they may give thanks to Thee. Thou hast bestowed upon us spiritual food and drink and eternal life through Thy Son. Above all we thank thee that Thou art powerful. To Thee be glory forever.

" Remember, Lord, Thy assembly, to rescue it from all evil and to bring it to completion in Thy love. Gather from the four winds the sanctified into Thine own kingdom which Thou hast prepared for them. Let grace come and let the world pass away. Hosannah to the God of David."

As I knelt in a silence enriched by an indescribable Presence I felt a strong arm move about my shoulders. Centurion Lentulus bent over me.

" Farewell, faithful soldier," said he.